Dear Katarina,

May you find joy
and inspiration in THE
NURSE SELF-CARE JOURNAL.

Rhoda M. Redulla
5-19-22

First edition: Printed 2022
ISBN 978-1-7365460-2-4

For inquiries, bulk purchases, personalization, or to report unauthorized use, please email info@beagreatnurse.com.

For more information about the author, please visit beagreatnurse.com.

Contributors

Jocelyn Espejo, BSN, RN, CCRN
Ariel Brettholz, BSN, RN
Katherine Moon, BSN, RN
Rose Gallagher, MBE
Kimberly Gallub, MSN, RN, CGRN
Larissa Morgan, MSN, RN, NPD-BC
Paul Fragante, RN

You always take care of others. Now, let's take care of you! Let this self-care journal guide you in your journey to joy, positivity, and resilience. Each week, commit to pausing and reflecting on what you have done to take care of yourself. Be inspired with the examples and quotes shared by fellow nurses. Enjoy your self-care journey!

Self-care is giving others the best of you, instead of what's left of you.
-Katie Reed

Week 1

How did I do on sleep?

_____

_____

What were some of the healthy eating choices I made?

_____

_____

What physical activity/ies did I do this week? (Did I spend time outdoors?)

_____

_____

What's one way that I can spread light to others?

_____

_____

How have I cared for myself this week?

_____

_____

What is something simple that I am looking forward to?

_____

_____

Week 1

These are the positive phrases I will invite into myself:

_____

_____

_____

What's something I'm really proud of myself for this week?

_____

_____

_____

What are three things that I am thankful for this week?

_____

_____

What stress did I experience & how did I overcome it?

_____

_____

_____

What was something I did for fun? Or that gave me joy?

_____

_____

What made me feel grounded or in control?

_____

_____

Week 2

How did I do on sleep?

_____

_____

What were some of the healthy eating choices I made?

_____

_____

What physical activity/ies did I do this week? (Did I spend time outdoors?)

_____

_____

What's one way that I can spread light to others?

_____

_____

How have I cared for myself this week?

_____

_____

What is something simple that I am looking forward to?

_____

_____

Week 2

These are the positive phrases I will invite into myself:

_____

_____

_____

What's something I'm really proud of myself for this week?

_____

_____

_____

What are three things that I am thankful for this week?

_____

_____

What stress did I experience & how did I overcome it?

_____

_____

_____

What was something I did for fun? Or that gave me joy?

_____

_____

What made me feel grounded or in control?

_____

_____

Week 3

How did I do on sleep?

_____

_____

What were some of the healthy eating choices I made?

_____

_____

What physical activity/ies did I do this week? (Did I spend time outdoors?)

_____

_____

What's one way that I can spread light to others?

_____

_____

How have I cared for myself this week?

_____

_____

What is something simple that I am looking forward to?

_____

_____

Week 3

These are the positive phrases I will invite into myself:

_____

_____

_____

What's something I'm really proud of myself for this week?

_____

_____

_____

What are three things that I am thankful for this week?

_____

_____

What stress did I experience & how did I overcome it?

_____

_____

_____

What was something I did for fun? Or that gave me joy?

_____

_____

What made me feel grounded or in control?

_____

_____

Artwork by: Jocelyn Espejo, BSN, RN, CCRN
Retired Critical Care Nurse

Breathe. Let go. And remind yourself that this very moment is the one you have for sure.
-Oprah Winfrey

Week 4

How did I do on sleep?

_____

_____

What were some of the healthy eating choices I made?

_____

_____

What physical activity/ies did I do this week? (Did I spend time outdoors?)

_____

_____

What's one way that I can spread light to others?

_____

_____

How have I cared for myself this week?

_____

_____

What is something simple that I am looking forward to?

_____

_____

Week 4

These are the positive phrases I will invite into myself:

_____

_____

_____

What's something I'm really proud of myself for this week?

_____

_____

What are three things that I am thankful for this week?

_____

_____

What stress did I experience & how did I overcome it?

_____

_____

_____

What was something I did for fun? Or that gave me joy?

_____

_____

What made me feel grounded or in control?

_____

_____

Week 5

How did I do on sleep?

_____

_____

What were some of the healthy eating choices I made?

_____

_____

What physical activity/ies did I do this week? (Did I spend time outdoors?)

_____

_____

What's one way that I can spread light to others?

_____

_____

How have I cared for myself this week?

_____

_____

What is something simple that I am looking forward to?

_____

_____

Week 5

These are the positive phrases I will invite into myself:

_____

_____

_____

What's something I'm really proud of myself for this week?

_____

_____

_____

What are three things that I am thankful for this week?

_____

_____

What stress did I experience & how did I overcome it?

_____

_____

_____

What was something I did for fun? Or that gave me joy?

_____

_____

What made me feel grounded or in control?

_____

_____

Week 6

How did I do on sleep?

_____

_____

What were some of the healthy eating choices I made?

_____

_____

What physical activity/ies did I do this week? (Did I spend time outdoors?)

_____

_____

What's one way that I can spread light to others?

_____

_____

How have I cared for myself this week?

_____

_____

What is something simple that I am looking forward to?

_____

_____

Week 6

These are the positive phrases I will invite into myself:

_____

_____

_____

What's something I'm really proud of myself for this week?

_____

_____

_____

What are three things that I am thankful for this week?

_____

_____

What stress did I experience & how did I overcome it?

_____

_____

_____

What was something I did for fun? Or that gave me joy?

_____

_____

What made me feel grounded or in control?

_____

_____

Week 7

How did I do on sleep?

_____

_____

What were some of the healthy eating choices I made?

_____

_____

What physical activity/ies did I do this week? (Did I spend time outdoors?)

_____

_____

What's one way that I can spread light to others?

_____

_____

How have I cared for myself this week?

_____

_____

What is something simple that I am looking forward to?

_____

_____

Week 7

These are the positive phrases I will invite into myself:

_____

_____

_____

What's something I'm really proud of myself for this week?

_____

_____

_____

What are three things that I am thankful for this week?

_____

_____

What stress did I experience & how did I overcome it?

_____

_____

_____

What was something I did for fun? Or that gave me joy?

_____

_____

What made me feel grounded or in control?

_____

_____

Watch yourself bloom.

What was something I did for fun?

A few weeks ago, I went to a drive-in movie theatre in Brooklyn, which also had a beautiful view of the New York City skyline. I was so excited to be watching a movie on a big screen while eating popcorn!

- Ariel Brettholz, BSN, RN (Pediatric Nurse)

Week 8

How did I do on sleep?

_____

_____

What were some of the healthy eating choices I made?

_____

_____

What physical activity/ies did I do this week? (Did I spend time outdoors?)

_____

_____

What's one way that I can spread light to others?

_____

_____

How have I cared for myself this week?

_____

_____

What is something simple that I am looking forward to?

_____

_____

Week 8

These are the positive phrases I will invite into myself:

_____

_____

_____

What's something I'm really proud of myself for this week?

_____

_____

_____

What are three things that I am thankful for this week?

_____

_____

What stress did I experience & how did I overcome it?

_____

_____

_____

What was something I did for fun? Or that gave me joy?

_____

_____

What made me feel grounded or in control?

_____

_____

Week 9

These are the positive phrases I will invite into myself:

_____

_____

_____

What's something I'm really proud of myself for this week?

_____

_____

_____

What are three things that I am thankful for this week?

_____

_____

What stress did I experience & how did I overcome it?

_____

_____

_____

What was something I did for fun? Or that gave me joy?

_____

_____

What made me feel grounded or in control?

_____

_____

Week 9

How did I do on sleep?

_____

_____

What were some of the healthy eating choices I made?

_____

_____

What physical activity/ies did I do this week? (Did I spend time outdoors?)

_____

_____

What's one way that I can spread light to others?

_____

_____

How have I cared for myself this week?

_____

_____

What is something simple that I am looking forward to?

_____

_____

Week 10

How did I do on sleep?

_____

_____

What were some of the healthy eating choices I made?

_____

_____

What physical activity/ies did I do this week? (Did I spend time outdoors?)

_____

_____

What's one way that I can spread light to others?

_____

_____

How have I cared for myself this week?

_____

_____

What is something simple that I am looking forward to?

_____

_____

Week 10

These are the positive phrases I will invite into myself:

_____

_____

_____

What's something I'm really proud of myself for this week?

_____

_____

_____

What are three things that I am thankful for this week?

_____

_____

_____

What stress did I experience & how did I overcome it?

_____

_____

_____

What was something I did for fun? Or that gave me joy?

_____

_____

What made me feel grounded or in control?

_____

_____

Week 11

How did I do on sleep?

_____

_____

What were some of the healthy eating choices I made?

_____

_____

What physical activity/ies did I do this week? (Did I spend time outdoors?)

_____

_____

What's one way that I can spread light to others?

_____

_____

How have I cared for myself this week?

_____

_____

What is something simple that I am looking forward to?

_____

_____

Week 11

These are the positive phrases I will invite into myself:

_____

_____

_____

What's something I'm really proud of myself for this week?

_____

_____

_____

What are three things that I am thankful for this week?

_____

_____

What stress did I experience & how did I overcome it?

_____

_____

_____

What was something I did for fun? Or that gave me joy?

_____

_____

What made me feel grounded or in control?

_____

_____

When I feel overwhelmed, I close my eyes and take a deep breath.

Artwork by: Katherine Moon, BSN, RN
(CICU)
katmoonlives.com

Week 12

How did I do on sleep?

_____

_____

What were some of the healthy eating choices I made?

_____

_____

What physical activity/ies did I do this week? (Did I spend time outdoors?)

_____

_____

What's one way that I can spread light to others?

_____

_____

How have I cared for myself this week?

_____

_____

What is something simple that I am looking forward to?

_____

_____

Week 12

These are the positive phrases I will invite into myself:

_____

_____

_____

What's something I'm really proud of myself for this week?

_____

_____

_____

What are three things that I am thankful for this week?

_____

_____

What stress did I experience & how did I overcome it?

_____

_____

_____

What was something I did for fun? Or that gave me joy?

_____

_____

What made me feel grounded or in control?

_____

_____

Week 13

How did I do on sleep?

_____

_____

What were some of the healthy eating choices I made?

_____

_____

What physical activity/ies did I do this week? (Did I spend time outdoors?)

_____

_____

What's one way that I can spread light to others?

_____

_____

How have I cared for myself this week?

_____

_____

What is something simple that I am looking forward to?

_____

_____

Week 13

These are the positive phrases I will invite into myself:

_____

_____

_____

What's something I'm really proud of myself for this week?

_____

_____

_____

What are three things that I am thankful for this week?

_____

_____

What stress did I experience & how did I overcome it?

_____

_____

_____

What was something I did for fun? Or that gave me joy?

_____

_____

What made me feel grounded or in control?

_____

_____

Week 14

How did I do on sleep?

_____

_____

What were some of the healthy eating choices I made?

_____

_____

What physical activity/ies did I do this week? (Did I spend time outdoors?)

_____

_____

What's one way that I can spread light to others?

_____

_____

How have I cared for myself this week?

_____

_____

What is something simple that I am looking forward to?

_____

_____

Week 14

These are the positive phrases I will invite into myself:

_____

_____

_____

What's something I'm really proud of myself for this week?

_____

_____

_____

What are three things that I am thankful for this week?

_____

_____

What stress did I experience & how did I overcome it?

_____

_____

_____

What was something I did for fun? Or that gave me joy?

_____

_____

What made me feel grounded or in control?

_____

_____

Nurses who have a strong sense of self and caring will provide holistic patient care grounded in caring values.

- Marian C. Turkel & Marilyn A. Ray

Week 15

How did I do on sleep?

_____

_____

What were some of the healthy eating choices I made?

_____

_____

What physical activity/ies did I do this week? (Did I spend time outdoors?)

_____

_____

What's one way that I can spread light to others?

_____

_____

How have I cared for myself this week?

_____

_____

What is something simple that I am looking forward to?

_____

_____

Week 15

These are the positive phrases I will invite into myself:

_____

_____

_____

What's something I'm really proud of myself for this week?

_____

_____

_____

What are three things that I am thankful for this week?

_____

_____

What stress did I experience & how did I overcome it?

_____

_____

_____

What was something I did for fun? Or that gave me joy?

_____

_____

What made me feel grounded or in control?

_____

_____

Week 16

How did I do on sleep?

_____

_____

What were some of the healthy eating choices I made?

_____

_____

What physical activity/ies did I do this week? (Did I spend time outdoors?)

_____

_____

What's one way that I can spread light to others?

_____

_____

How have I cared for myself this week?

_____

_____

What is something simple that I am looking forward to?

_____

_____

Week 16

These are the positive phrases I will invite into myself:

_____

_____

_____

What's something I'm really proud of myself for this week?

_____

_____

_____

What are three things that I am thankful for this week?

_____

_____

What stress did I experience & how did I overcome it?

_____

_____

_____

What was something I did for fun? Or that gave me joy?

_____

_____

What made me feel grounded or in control?

_____

_____

Week 17

How did I do on sleep?

_____

_____

What were some of the healthy eating choices I made?

_____

_____

What physical activity/ies did I do this week? (Did I spend time outdoors?)

_____

_____

What's one way that I can spread light to others?

_____

_____

How have I cared for myself this week?

_____

_____

What is something simple that I am looking forward to?

_____

_____

Week 17

These are the positive phrases I will invite into myself:

_____

_____

_____

What's something I'm really proud of myself for this week?

_____

_____

_____

What are three things that I am thankful for this week?

_____

_____

What stress did I experience & how did I overcome it?

_____

_____

_____

What was something I did for fun? Or that gave me joy?

_____

_____

What made me feel grounded or in control?

_____

_____

Week 18

How did I do on sleep?

_____

_____

What were some of the healthy eating choices I made?

_____

_____

What physical activity/ies did I do this week? (Did I spend time outdoors?)

_____

_____

What's one way that I can spread light to others?

_____

_____

How have I cared for myself this week?

_____

_____

What is something simple that I am looking forward to?

_____

_____

Week 18

These are the positive phrases I will invite into myself:

_____

_____

_____

What's something I'm really proud of myself for this week?

_____

_____

_____

What are three things that I am thankful for this week?

_____

_____

What stress did I experience & how did I overcome it?

_____

_____

_____

What was something I did for fun? Or that gave me joy?

_____

_____

What made me feel grounded or in control?

_____

_____

What's something I'm really proud of myself for this week?
Publishing the Infection Prevention Control guidance evidence review — an exceptionally well written report which we (at the Royal College of Nursing) commissioned.

Rose Gallagher MBE
Professional Lead Infection
Prevention and Control/Antibiotic
Microbial Resistance

Week 19

How did I do on sleep?

_____

_____

What were some of the healthy eating choices I made?

_____

_____

What physical activity/ies did I do this week? (Did I spend time outdoors?)

_____

_____

What's one way that I can spread light to others?

_____

_____

How have I cared for myself this week?

_____

_____

What is something simple that I am looking forward to?

_____

_____

Week 19

These are the positive phrases I will invite into myself:

_____

_____

_____

What's something I'm really proud of myself for this week?

_____

_____

_____

What are three things that I am thankful for this week?

_____

_____

What stress did I experience & how did I overcome it?

_____

_____

_____

What was something I did for fun? Or that gave me joy?

_____

_____

What made me feel grounded or in control?

_____

_____

Week 20

How did I do on sleep?

_____

_____

What were some of the healthy eating choices I made?

_____

_____

What physical activity/ies did I do this week? (Did I spend time outdoors?)

_____

_____

What's one way that I can spread light to others?

_____

_____

How have I cared for myself this week?

_____

_____

What is something simple that I am looking forward to?

_____

_____

Week 20

These are the positive phrases I will invite into myself:

_____

_____

_____

What's something I'm really proud of myself for this week?

_____

_____

_____

What are three things that I am thankful for this week?

_____

_____

What stress did I experience & how did I overcome it?

_____

_____

_____

What was something I did for fun? Or that gave me joy?

_____

_____

What made me feel grounded or in control?

_____

_____

Week 21

How did I do on sleep?

_____

_____

What were some of the healthy eating choices I made?

_____

_____

What physical activity/ies did I do this week? (Did I spend time outdoors?)

_____

_____

What's one way that I can spread light to others?

_____

_____

How have I cared for myself this week?

_____

_____

What is something simple that I am looking forward to?

_____

_____

Week 21

These are the positive phrases I will invite into myself:

_____

_____

_____

What's something I'm really proud of myself for this week?

_____

_____

_____

What are three things that I am thankful for this week?

_____

_____

What stress did I experience & how did I overcome it?

_____

_____

_____

What was something I did for fun? Or that gave me joy?

_____

_____

What made me feel grounded or in control?

_____

_____

How have I cared for myself this week?

I love to do puzzles. I started to do them during the COVID-19 quarantine in the Spring of 2020. It has become very therapeutic for me.

- Ariel Brettholz, BSN, RN
(Pediatric Nurse)

Ariel won in the 2020 Nurses' Week Self-Care Selfie of her hospital. Along with other winners, she was featured in the American Nurses Association (ANA) Healthy Nurse Healthy Nation blog.

Did you notice the pink hue of the sunset, the flock of birds above you, & the warm air touching your skin as you were driving home from work?

Week 22

How did I do on sleep?

_____

_____

What were some of the healthy eating choices I made?

_____

_____

What physical activity/ies did I do this week? (Did I spend time outdoors?)

_____

_____

What's one way that I can spread light to others?

_____

_____

How have I cared for myself this week?

_____

_____

What is something simple that I am looking forward to?

_____

_____

Week 22

These are the positive phrases I will invite into myself:

_____

_____

_____

What's something I'm really proud of myself for this week?

_____

_____

What are three things that I am thankful for this week?

_____

_____

What stress did I experience & how did I overcome it?

_____

_____

_____

What was something I did for fun? Or that gave me joy?

_____

_____

What made me feel grounded or in control?

_____

_____

Week 23

How did I do on sleep?

_____

_____

What were some of the healthy eating choices I made?

_____

_____

What physical activity/ies did I do this week? (Did I spend time outdoors?)

_____

_____

What's one way that I can spread light to others?

_____

_____

How have I cared for myself this week?

_____

_____

What is something simple that I am looking forward to?

_____

_____

Week 23

These are the positive phrases I will invite into myself:

_____

_____

_____

What's something I'm really proud of myself for this week?

_____

_____

_____

What are three things that I am thankful for this week?

_____

_____

What stress did I experience & how did I overcome it?

_____

_____

_____

What was something I did for fun? Or that gave me joy?

_____

_____

What made me feel grounded or in control?

_____

_____

Week 24

How did I do on sleep?

_____

_____

What were some of the healthy eating choices I made?

_____

_____

What physical activity/ies did I do this week? (Did I spend time outdoors?)

_____

_____

What's one way that I can spread light to others?

_____

_____

How have I cared for myself this week?

_____

_____

What is something simple that I am looking forward to?

_____

_____

Week 24

These are the positive phrases I will invite into myself:

_____

_____

_____

What's something I'm really proud of myself for this week?

_____

_____

_____

What are three things that I am thankful for this week?

_____

_____

What stress did I experience & how did I overcome it?

_____

_____

_____

What was something I did for fun? Or that gave me joy?

_____

_____

What made me feel grounded or in control?

_____

_____

Week 25

How did I do on sleep?

_____

_____

What were some of the healthy eating choices I made?

_____

_____

What physical activity/ies did I do this week? (Did I spend time outdoors?)

_____

_____

What's one way that I can spread light to others?

_____

_____

How have I cared for myself this week?

_____

_____

What is something simple that I am looking forward to?

_____

_____

Week 25

These are the positive phrases I will invite into myself:

_____

_____

_____

What's something I'm really proud of myself for this week?

_____

_____

_____

What are three things that I am thankful for this week?

_____

_____

_____

What stress did I experience & how did I overcome it?

_____

_____

_____

What was something I did for fun? Or that gave me joy?

_____

_____

What made me feel grounded or in control?

_____

_____

Sam Martinez
Pink Skies, 2020
Digital Watercolor
NYP Weill Cornell Dialysis unit in the time of COVID-19 pandemic
In memory of Brigitte Hebert RN

Artwork by: Sam Martinez, BSN, RN, CNN
Dialysis Senior Staff Nurse

Week 26

How did I do on sleep?

_____

_____

What were some of the healthy eating choices I made?

_____

_____

What physical activity/ies did I do this week? (Did I spend time outdoors?)

_____

_____

What's one way that I can spread light to others?

_____

_____

How have I cared for myself this week?

_____

_____

What is something simple that I am looking forward to?

_____

_____

Week 26

These are the positive phrases I will invite into myself:

_____

_____

_____

What's something I'm really proud of myself for this week?

_____

_____

_____

What are three things that I am thankful for this week?

_____

_____

What stress did I experience & how did I overcome it?

_____

_____

_____

What was something I did for fun? Or that gave me joy?

_____

_____

What made me feel grounded or in control?

_____

_____

Week 27

How did I do on sleep?

_____

_____

What were some of the healthy eating choices I made?

_____

_____

What physical activity/ies did I do this week? (Did I spend time outdoors?)

_____

_____

What's one way that I can spread light to others?

_____

_____

How have I cared for myself this week?

_____

_____

What is something simple that I am looking forward to?

_____

_____

Week 27

These are the positive phrases I will invite into myself:

_____

_____

_____

What's something I'm really proud of myself for this week?

_____

_____

_____

What are three things that I am thankful for this week?

_____

_____

What stress did I experience & how did I overcome it?

_____

_____

_____

What was something I did for fun? Or that gave me joy?

_____

_____

What made me feel grounded or in control?

_____

_____

Week 28

How did I do on sleep?

_____

_____

What were some of the healthy eating choices I made?

_____

_____

What physical activity/ies did I do this week? (Did I spend time outdoors?)

_____

_____

What's one way that I can spread light to others?

_____

_____

How have I cared for myself this week?

_____

_____

What is something simple that I am looking forward to?

_____

_____

Week 28

These are the positive phrases I will invite into myself:

_____

_____

_____

What's something I'm really proud of myself for this week?

_____

_____

_____

What are three things that I am thankful for this week?

_____

_____

What stress did I experience & how did I overcome it?

_____

_____

_____

What was something I did for fun? Or that gave me joy?

_____

_____

What made me feel grounded or in control?

_____

_____

What are three good things that happened this week?

- *My unit reverted back to an endoscopy unit from a month long stint as a COVID positive inpatient unit.*
- *My son made a team he was trying out for.*
- *I was able to get a decent amount of sleep.*

- Kimberly Gallub, MSN, RN, CGRN (Nurse Manager, Endoscopy Unit)

Fill your bucket

Week 29

How did I do on sleep?

_____

_____

What were some of the healthy eating choices I made?

_____

_____

What physical activity/ies did I do this week? (Did I spend time outdoors?)

_____

_____

What's one way that I can spread light to others?

_____

_____

How have I cared for myself this week?

_____

_____

What is something simple that I am looking forward to?

_____

_____

Week 29

These are the positive phrases I will invite into myself:

_____

_____

_____

What's something I'm really proud of myself for this week?

_____

_____

_____

What are three things that I am thankful for this week?

_____

_____

What stress did I experience & how did I overcome it?

_____

_____

_____

What was something I did for fun? Or that gave me joy?

_____

_____

What made me feel grounded or in control?

_____

_____

Week 30

How did I do on sleep?

_____

_____

What were some of the healthy eating choices I made?

_____

_____

What physical activity/ies did I do this week? (Did I spend time outdoors?)

_____

_____

What's one way that I can spread light to others?

_____

_____

How have I cared for myself this week?

_____

_____

What is something simple that I am looking forward to?

_____

_____

Week 30

These are the positive phrases I will invite into myself:

_____

_____

_____

What's something I'm really proud of myself for this week?

_____

_____

_____

What are three things that I am thankful for this week?

_____

_____

What stress did I experience & how did I overcome it?

_____

_____

_____

What was something I did for fun? Or that gave me joy?

_____

_____

What made me feel grounded or in control?

_____

_____

Week 31

How did I do on sleep?

_____

_____

What were some of the healthy eating choices I made?

_____

_____

What physical activity/ies did I do this week? (Did I spend time outdoors?)

_____

_____

What's one way that I can spread light to others?

_____

_____

How have I cared for myself this week?

_____

_____

What is something simple that I am looking forward to?

_____

_____

Week 31

These are the positive phrases I will invite into myself:

_____

_____

_____

What's something I'm really proud of myself for this week?

_____

_____

_____

What are three things that I am thankful for this week?

_____

_____

What stress did I experience & how did I overcome it?

_____

_____

_____

What was something I did for fun? Or that gave me joy?

_____

_____

What made me feel grounded or in control?

_____

_____

Week 32

How did I do on sleep?

_____

_____

What were some of the healthy eating choices I made?

_____

_____

What physical activity/ies did I do this week? (Did I spend time outdoors?)

_____

_____

What's one way that I can spread light to others?

_____

_____

How have I cared for myself this week?

_____

_____

What is something simple that I am looking forward to?

_____

_____

Week 32

These are the positive phrases I will invite into myself:

_____

_____

_____

What's something I'm really proud of myself for this week?

_____

_____

_____

What are three things that I am thankful for this week?

_____

_____

What stress did I experience & how did I overcome it?

_____

_____

_____

What was something I did for fun? Or that gave me joy?

_____

_____

What made me feel grounded or in control?

_____

_____

What made me feel grounded or in control?

One of my words for the year is "lead!" I feel in control when I lead the things in my life I have control over instead of having them lead me. One major example ie being prepared (including mentally) for upcoming events I have on my calendar. If I can prepare ahead of time I feel so grounded and in control.

-Larissa Morgan, MSN, RN, NPD-BC (Manager, Clinical Talent Acquisition)

Week 33

How did I do on sleep?

_____

_____

What were some of the healthy eating choices I made?

_____

_____

What physical activity/ies did I do this week? (Did I spend time outdoors?)

_____

_____

What's one way that I can spread light to others?

_____

_____

How have I cared for myself this week?

_____

_____

What is something simple that I am looking forward to?

_____

_____

Week 33

These are the positive phrases I will invite into myself:

_____

_____

_____

What's something I'm really proud of myself for this week?

_____

_____

_____

What are three things that I am thankful for this week?

_____

_____

What stress did I experience & how did I overcome it?

_____

_____

_____

What was something I did for fun? Or that gave me joy?

_____

_____

What made me feel grounded or in control?

_____

_____

Week 34

How did I do on sleep?

_____

_____

What were some of the healthy eating choices I made?

_____

_____

What physical activity/ies did I do this week? (Did I spend time outdoors?)

_____

_____

What's one way that I can spread light to others?

_____

_____

How have I cared for myself this week?

_____

_____

What is something simple that I am looking forward to?

_____

_____

Week 34

These are the positive phrases I will invite into myself:

_____

_____

_____

What's something I'm really proud of myself for this week?

_____

_____

_____

What are three things that I am thankful for this week?

_____

_____

What stress did I experience & how did I overcome it?

_____

_____

_____

What was something I did for fun? Or that gave me joy?

_____

_____

What made me feel grounded or in control?

_____

_____

What was a stressful thing that happened to me and how did I overcame it?

The most stressful thing to happen recently had to have been the unit reverting back to a Covid + unit, while maintaining the endoscopy unit. Our nursing team had to be divided between the endoscopy unit and staffing the COVID unit 24/7. There was not enough team members to handle both settings. The stress involved in trying to figure that out was overcome when the staff all pulled together and worked together to staff both units. It was teamwork at it's finest.

**- Kimberly Gallub, MSN, RN, CGRN
(Nurse Manager, Endoscopy Unit)**

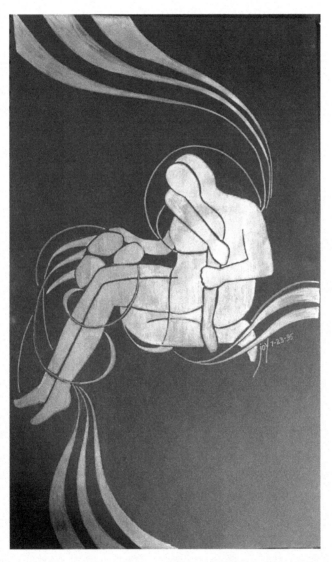

Artwork by: Jocelyn Espejo, BSN, RN, CCRN
Critical Care Nurse

Week 35

How did I do on sleep?

_____

_____

What were some of the healthy eating choices I made?

_____

_____

What physical activity/ies did I do this week? (Did I spend time outdoors?)

_____

_____

What's one way that I can spread light to others?

_____

_____

How have I cared for myself this week?

_____

_____

What is something simple that I am looking forward to?

_____

_____

Week 35

These are the positive phrases I will invite into myself:

_____

_____

_____

What's something I'm really proud of myself for this week?

_____

_____

_____

What are three things that I am thankful for this week?

_____

_____

What stress did I experience & how did I overcome it?

_____

_____

_____

What was something I did for fun? Or that gave me joy?

_____

_____

What made me feel grounded or in control?

_____

_____

Week 36

How did I do on sleep?

_____

_____

What were some of the healthy eating choices I made?

_____

_____

What physical activity/ies did I do this week? (Did I spend time outdoors?)

_____

_____

What's one way that I can spread light to others?

_____

_____

How have I cared for myself this week?

_____

_____

What is something simple that I am looking forward to?

_____

_____

Week 36

How did I do on sleep?

_____

_____

What were some of the healthy eating choices I made?

_____

_____

What physical activity/ies did I do this week? (Did I spend time outdoors?)

_____

_____

What's one way that I can spread light to others?

_____

_____

How have I cared for myself this week?

_____

_____

What is something simple that I am looking forward to?

_____

_____

Week 36

These are the positive phrases I will invite into myself:

_____

_____

_____

What's something I'm really proud of myself for this week?

_____

_____

_____

What are three things that I am thankful for this week?

_____

_____

What stress did I experience & how did I overcome it?

_____

_____

_____

What was something I did for fun? Or that gave me joy?

_____

_____

What made me feel grounded or in control?

_____

_____

What's something I'm really proud of myself for this week?

I have been using the NYPBeHealthy resources (wellness program of our hospital) and have been setting weekly mini-goals with a Wellness Coach to help alleviate stress and promote better sleep habits. Last week, we tried a bit of journaling, and this week it is trying to incorporate some 5-10 minute meditation sessions. This coming week, I will work on doing some meditative doodling (I've just been doing sitting meditation) and see how that helps. It is a small step, but with each day, month, and year, eventually you will have traveled a thousand miles ; it just takes that one small step each day and not empowering the voice of the inner-critic on a work in progress.

-Katherine Moon, BSN, RN
(CICU)

What do you do to take care of yourself?

So far I love the Chicago because most of the courses were flat. It was also in here that I was able to convince my wife to run the 5k with me a day before the marathon. I do it to improve my overall health, to challenge myself and for fun. It is also worthwhile to know that you are contributing to a cause when you are joining runs.Running not only made me strong physically to withstand the long hours of taking care of our patients. This is also my natural stress buster. I feel energized usually after I run.

-Paul Fragante, RN
(Dialysis)

Week 37

How did I do on sleep?

_____

_____

What were some of the healthy eating choices I made?

_____

_____

What physical activity/ies did I do this week? (Did I spend time outdoors?)

_____

_____

What's one way that I can spread light to others?

_____

_____

How have I cared for myself this week?

_____

_____

What is something simple that I am looking forward to?

_____

_____

Week 37

These are the positive phrases I will invite into myself:

_____

_____

_____

What's something I'm really proud of myself for this week?

_____

_____

_____

What are three things that I am thankful for this week?

_____

_____

What stress did I experience & how did I overcome it?

_____

_____

_____

What was something I did for fun? Or that gave me joy?

_____

_____

What made me feel grounded or in control?

_____

_____

Week 38

How did I do on sleep?

_____

_____

What were some of the healthy eating choices I made?

_____

_____

What physical activity/ies did I do this week? (Did I spend time outdoors?)

_____

_____

What's one way that I can spread light to others?

_____

_____

How have I cared for myself this week?

_____

_____

What is something simple that I am looking forward to?

_____

_____

Week 38

These are the positive phrases I will invite into myself:

_____

_____

_____

What's something I'm really proud of myself for this week?

_____

_____

_____

What are three things that I am thankful for this week?

_____

_____

What stress did I experience & how did I overcome it?

_____

_____

_____

What was something I did for fun? Or that gave me joy?

_____

_____

What made me feel grounded or in control?

_____

_____

Week 39

How did I do on sleep?

_____

_____

What were some of the healthy eating choices I made?

_____

_____

What physical activity/ies did I do this week? (Did I spend time outdoors?)

_____

_____

What's one way that I can spread light to others?

_____

_____

How have I cared for myself this week?

_____

_____

What is something simple that I am looking forward to?

_____

_____

Week 39

These are the positive phrases I will invite into myself:

_____

_____

_____

What's something I'm really proud of myself for this week?

_____

_____

_____

What are three things that I am thankful for this week?

_____

_____

What stress did I experience & how did I overcome it?

_____

_____

_____

What was something I did for fun? Or that gave me joy?

_____

_____

What made me feel grounded or in control?

_____

_____

What physical activity/ies did I do this week?
(Did I spend time outdoors?)

never intend to run marathons at first. Back home n the Philippines, I used to run just for fun. It was nly here in the US about 7 years ago that I thought of joining organized running to challenge myself. I did 2 major marathons the Chicago and New York. I will run the Berlin hopefully this September. I did a lot of half marathons and few marathons organized by cities like Atlantic and Washington DC

-Paul Fragante, RN
(Dialysis)

Week 40

How did I do on sleep?

_____

_____

What were some of the healthy eating choices I made?

_____

_____

What physical activity/ies did I do this week? (Did I spend time outdoors?)

_____

_____

What's one way that I can spread light to others?

_____

_____

How have I cared for myself this week?

_____

_____

What is something simple that I am looking forward to?

_____

_____

Week 40

These are the positive phrases I will invite into myself:

_____

_____

_____

What's something I'm really proud of myself for this week?

_____

_____

_____

What are three things that I am thankful for this week?

_____

_____

What stress did I experience & how did I overcome it?

_____

_____

_____

What was something I did for fun? Or that gave me joy?

_____

_____

What made me feel grounded or in control?

_____

_____

Week 41

How did I do on sleep?

_____

_____

What were some of the healthy eating choices I made?

_____

_____

What physical activity/ies did I do this week? (Did I spend time outdoors?)

_____

_____

What's one way that I can spread light to others?

_____

_____

How have I cared for myself this week?

_____

_____

What is something simple that I am looking forward to?

_____

_____

Week 41

These are the positive phrases I will invite into myself:

_____

_____

_____

What's something I'm really proud of myself for this week?

_____

_____

_____

What are three things that I am thankful for this week?

_____

_____

What stress did I experience & how did I overcome it?

_____

_____

_____

What was something I did for fun? Or that gave me joy?

_____

_____

What made me feel grounded or in control?

_____

_____

Week 42

How did I do on sleep?

_____

_____

What were some of the healthy eating choices I made?

_____

_____

What physical activity/ies did I do this week? (Did I spend time outdoors?)

_____

_____

What's one way that I can spread light to others?

_____

_____

How have I cared for myself this week?

_____

_____

What is something simple that I am looking forward to?

_____

_____

Week 42

These are the positive phrases I will invite into myself:

_____

_____

_____

What's something I'm really proud of myself for this week?

_____

_____

_____

What are three things that I am thankful for this week?

_____

_____

What stress did I experience & how did I overcome it?

_____

_____

_____

What was something I did for fun? Or that gave me joy?

_____

_____

What made me feel grounded or in control?

_____

_____

Week 43

How did I do on sleep?

_____

_____

What were some of the healthy eating choices I made?

_____

_____

What physical activity/ies did I do this week? (Did I spend time outdoors?)

_____

_____

What's one way that I can spread light to others?

_____

_____

How have I cared for myself this week?

_____

_____

What is something simple that I am looking forward to?

_____

_____

Week 43

These are the positive phrases I will invite into myself:

_____

_____

_____

What's something I'm really proud of myself for this week?

_____

_____

_____

What are three things that I am thankful for this week?

_____

_____

What stress did I experience & how did I overcome it?

_____

_____

_____

What was something I did for fun? Or that gave me joy?

_____

_____

What made me feel grounded or in control?

_____

_____

Week 44

How did I do on sleep?

_____

_____

What were some of the healthy eating choices I made?

_____

_____

What physical activity/ies did I do this week? (Did I spend time outdoors?)

_____

_____

What's one way that I can spread light to others?

_____

_____

How have I cared for myself this week?

_____

_____

What is something simple that I am looking forward to?

_____

_____

Week 44

These are the positive phrases I will invite into myself:

_____

_____

_____

What's something I'm really proud of myself for this week?

_____

_____

_____

What are three things that I am thankful for this week?

_____

_____

What stress did I experience & how did I overcome it?

_____

_____

_____

What was something I did for fun? Or that gave me joy?

_____

_____

What made me feel grounded or in control?

_____

_____

What's one way that I can spread light to others?

For me, making artwork has been a way to keep the light inside of myself going; it clears my mind, helps me take a step back, and plants new seeds of hope. This year especially, it has been key in processing the loss of life and essential in helping me grieve. With a blank canvas, anything is possible; a new beginning for each day and sharing this possibility with others.

-Katherine Moon, BSN, RN
(CICU)
katmoonlives.com

Week 45

How did I do on sleep?

_____

_____

What were some of the healthy eating choices I made?

_____

_____

What physical activity/ies did I do this week? (Did I spend time outdoors?)

_____

_____

What's one way that I can spread light to others?

_____

_____

How have I cared for myself this week?

_____

_____

What is something simple that I am looking forward to?

_____

_____

Week 45

These are the positive phrases I will invite into myself:

_____

_____

_____

What's something I'm really proud of myself for this week?

_____

_____

_____

What are three things that I am thankful for this week?

_____

_____

What stress did I experience & how did I overcome it?

_____

_____

_____

What was something I did for fun? Or that gave me joy?

_____

_____

What made me feel grounded or in control?

_____

_____

Week 46

How did I do on sleep?

_____

_____

What were some of the healthy eating choices I made?

_____

_____

What physical activity/ies did I do this week? (Did I spend time outdoors?)

_____

_____

What's one way that I can spread light to others?

_____

_____

How have I cared for myself this week?

_____

_____

What is something simple that I am looking forward to?

_____

_____

Week 46

These are the positive phrases I will invite into myself:

_____

_____

_____

What's something I'm really proud of myself for this week?

_____

_____

_____

What are three things that I am thankful for this week?

_____

_____

What stress did I experience & how did I overcome it?

_____

_____

_____

What was something I did for fun? Or that gave me joy?

_____

_____

What made me feel grounded or in control?

_____

_____

Week 47

How did I do on sleep?

_____

_____

What were some of the healthy eating choices I made?

_____

_____

What physical activity/ies did I do this week? (Did I spend time outdoors?)

_____

_____

What's one way that I can spread light to others?

_____

_____

How have I cared for myself this week?

_____

_____

What is something simple that I am looking forward to?

_____

_____

Week 47

These are the positive phrases I will invite into myself:

_____

_____

_____

What's something I'm really proud of myself for this week?

_____

_____

_____

What are three things that I am thankful for this week?

_____

_____

What stress did I experience & how did I overcome it?

_____

_____

_____

What was something I did for fun? Or that gave me joy?

_____

_____

What made me feel grounded or in control?

_____

_____

Artwork by: Sam Martinez, BSN, RN, CNN
Dialysis Senior Staff Nurse

Week 48

How did I do on sleep?

_____

_____

What were some of the healthy eating choices I made?

_____

_____

What physical activity/ies did I do this week? (Did I spend time outdoors?)

_____

_____

What's one way that I can spread light to others?

_____

_____

How have I cared for myself this week?

_____

_____

What is something simple that I am looking forward to?

_____

_____

Week 48

These are the positive phrases I will invite into myself:

_____

_____

_____

What's something I'm really proud of myself for this week?

_____

_____

_____

What are three things that I am thankful for this week?

_____

_____

What stress did I experience & how did I overcome it?

_____

_____

_____

What was something I did for fun? Or that gave me joy?

_____

_____

What made me feel grounded or in control?

_____

_____

Week 49

How did I do on sleep?

_____

_____

What were some of the healthy eating choices I made?

_____

_____

What physical activity/ies did I do this week? (Did I spend time outdoors?)

_____

_____

What's one way that I can spread light to others?

_____

_____

How have I cared for myself this week?

_____

_____

What is something simple that I am looking forward to?

_____

_____

Week 49

These are the positive phrases I will invite into myself:

_____

_____

_____

What's something I'm really proud of myself for this week?

_____

_____

What are three things that I am thankful for this week?

_____

_____

What stress did I experience & how did I overcome it?

_____

_____

_____

What was something I did for fun? Or that gave me joy?

_____

_____

What made me feel grounded or in control?

_____

_____

What was something I did do for fun? Or gave me joy?
At home: I spent an hour in my garden moving plants and tending to seeds on a sunny day

At work: I saw a fantastic tweet on the day the children returned to school with an image of a notice saying there was an outbreak of head lice 23 minutes after the children has been back in school. It made me laugh

Rose Gallagher MBE
Professional Lead Infection
Prevention and Control/Antibiotic
Microbial Resistance

Week 50

How did I do on sleep?

_____

_____

What were some of the healthy eating choices I made?

_____

_____

What physical activity/ies did I do this week? (Did I spend time outdoors?)

_____

_____

What's one way that I can spread light to others?

_____

_____

How have I cared for myself this week?

_____

_____

What is something simple that I am looking forward to?

_____

_____

Week 50

These are the positive phrases I will invite into myself:

_____

_____

_____

What's something I'm really proud of myself for this week?

_____

_____

_____

What are three things that I am thankful for this week?

_____

_____

What stress did I experience & how did I overcome it?

_____

_____

_____

What was something I did for fun? Or that gave me joy?

_____

_____

What made me feel grounded or in control?

_____

_____

Week 51

How did I do on sleep?

_____

_____

What were some of the healthy eating choices I made?

_____

_____

What physical activity/ies did I do this week? (Did I spend time outdoors?)

_____

_____

What's one way that I can spread light to others?

_____

_____

How have I cared for myself this week?

_____

_____

What is something simple that I am looking forward to?

_____

_____

Week 51

These are the positive phrases I will invite into myself:

_____

_____

_____

What's something I'm really proud of myself for this week?

_____

_____

_____

What are three things that I am thankful for this week?

_____

_____

What stress did I experience & how did I overcome it?

_____

_____

_____

What was something I did for fun? Or that gave me joy?

_____

_____

What made me feel grounded or in control?

_____

_____

Week 52

How did I do on sleep?

_____

_____

What were some of the healthy eating choices I made?

_____

_____

What physical activity/ies did I do this week? (Did I spend time outdoors?)

_____

_____

What's one way that I can spread light to others?

_____

_____

How have I cared for myself this week?

_____

_____

What is something simple that I am looking forward to?

_____

_____

Week 52

These are the positive phrases I will invite into myself:

_____

_____

_____

What's something I'm really proud of myself for this week?

_____

_____

_____

What are three things that I am thankful for this week?

_____

_____

What stress did I experience & how did I overcome it?

_____

_____

_____

What was something I did for fun? Or that gave me joy?

_____

_____

What made me feel grounded or in control?

_____

_____

CPSIA information can be obtained
at www.ICGtesting.com
Printed in the USA
JSHW011905260322
24273JS00005B/101